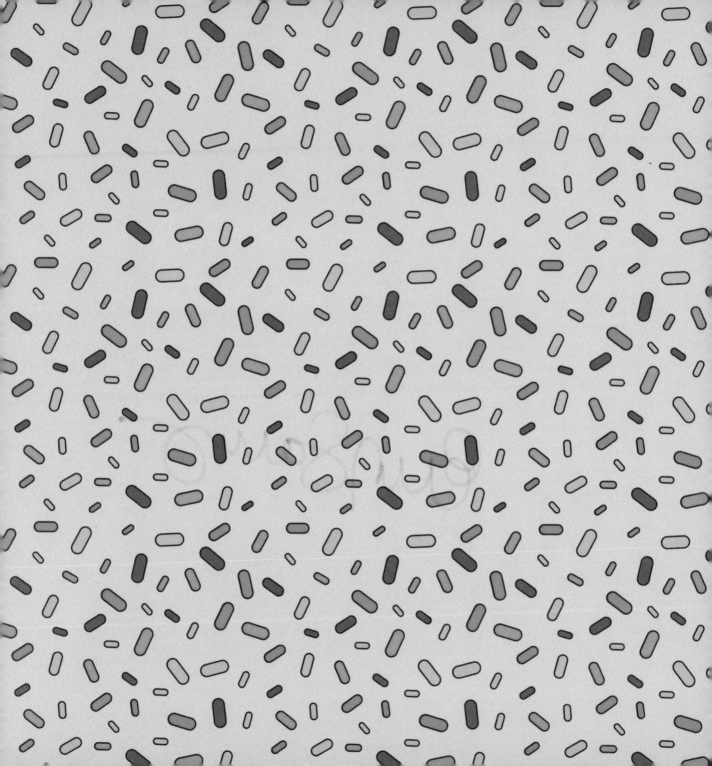

CUPCAKES EVERYWHERE!

One Sweet Tale of Overcoming Infertility

STORY BY
Erin Sarris

ILLUSTRATIONS BY
Bessa

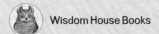 Wisdom House Books

THIS BOOK BELONGS TO:

_____

Your Name

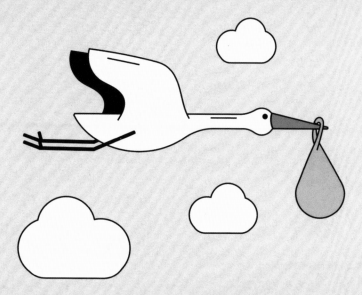

CUPCAKES EVERYWHERE!

Published by Wisdom House Books, Inc. - Chapel Hill, North Carolina 27517, USA
www.wisdomhousebooks.com

Wisdom House Books is committed to excellence in the publishing industry.
Book design copyright ©2024 by Wisdom House Books.
All rights reserved.

Cover and Interior Illustration by Barbora Dzadík Kmecová
Cover and Interior design by Ted Ruybal
100% Human Made. No AI used.
Published in the United States of America
Printed in Canada

Hardback ISBN: 979-8-9901641-0-9
LCCN: 2024903828

HEA045000 | HEALTH & FITNESS / Fertility & Infertility
HEA041000 | HEALTH & FITNESS / Pregnancy & Childbirth
JUV013040 | JUVENILE FICTION / Family / New Baby

First Edition
25 24 23 22 21 20 / 10 9 8 7 6 5 4 3 2 1

To Noelle, Sydney and Connor,

along with every cupcake that needed
a little extra time.

And to Meni:

The only person on the planet
I'd want as my co-baker.

THE CUPCAKES

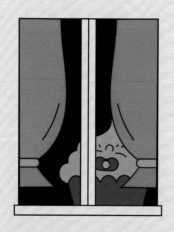
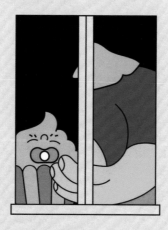
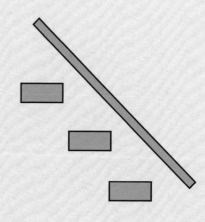

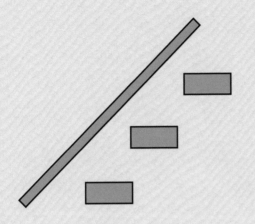

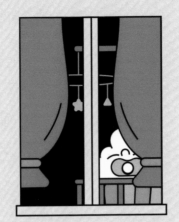

WERE EVERYWHERE!

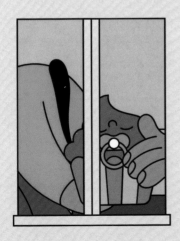

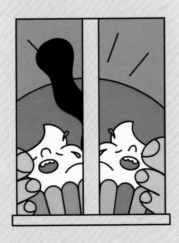

On the sidewalk.

In the grocery store.

At the library.

And *especially* in all the restaurants.

There were pink cupcakes.

Green cupcakes.

Polka dotted cupcakes.

Tie-dyed cupcakes.

Sprinkled cupcakes.

Some people had two or three
or even four at a time.

THE CUPCAKES

WERE EVERYWHERE!

One day, we decided we wanted one too.

"Excuse me?" we asked.

"Where could we get one of those cupcakes?"

"Oh, it's easy," they told us.

"Just go home and bake one!"

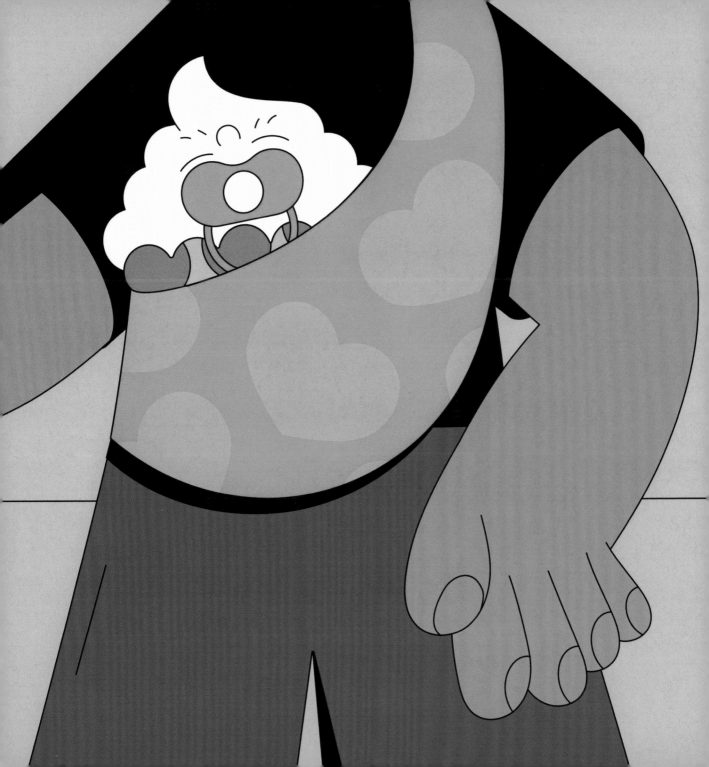

So we got all the ingredients.

Eggs, flour, sugar, butter.

We even got sprinkles.

And then we went home – and waited.

And waited.

And waited.

And waited some more.

Months went by,
and not even a mini cupcake turned out.

A whole year passed,
and we were no closer to meeting our cupcake.

"Was something wrong with our butter?"
we wondered.

"Maybe we used the wrong type of flour."

And meanwhile . . .

After a while, we started to feel pretty grumpy.

"Why is it so hard to get even *one* cupcake?"
we said to each other.

"Cupcakes make life sweet. Most people can make them at home! Why can't we?"

It seemed like we were mad, but we were actually sad.

Because . . .

But ours was nowhere to be found.

People didn't know what to say, so they said:

"Are you sure you're mixing them right?"

"My friend used a special type of sugar for her cupcake."

"You can have some of my cupcakes, I have too many."

"If you could just relax, then they'd turn out."

"Maybe your eggs are spoiled."

Or "I guess you just weren't meant to have a cupcake."

We didn't like this very much.

But then one day, someone said,

"Well if you can't bake a cupcake at home, why don't you try the special bakery?"

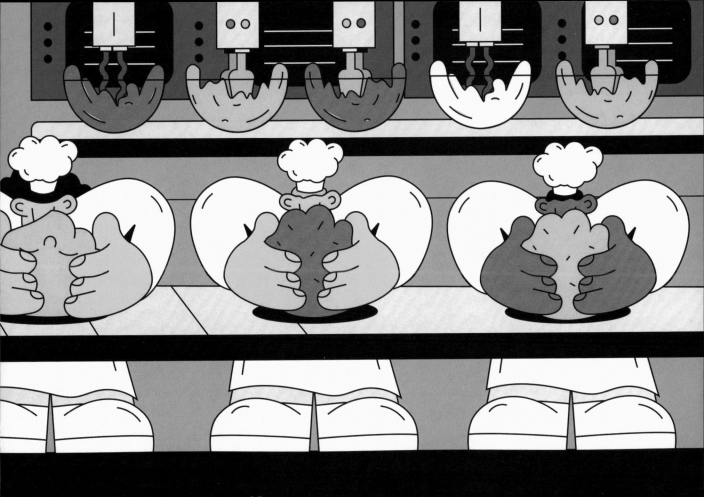

So off we went.
This was not like at home.

It wasn't easy.
We were afraid we might not even get a cupcake in the end.

It wasn't cheap.
The cupcakes cost a lot more than the ones you make at home.

It wasn't quick.
We waited. And waited. And waited some more.

Sometimes we had to start the entire batch over.

But one day we got a phone call.

Not just any phone call.

THE phone call.

Our cupcake was out of the oven, and it was perfect.

We ran to the bakery, giddy as can be.

And on the way, we couldn't help but notice that . . .

And finally, we had baked one of our very own.

A Note From The Author

5 total rounds of IVF.
Dozens of baby showers spent blinking back tears.
Over 500 injections and countless pills.
More blood draw appointments than I could even start to count.
1 heartbreaking early loss.
Too many phone calls where we waited all day to hear, "Better luck next time."

"Cupcakes Everywhere!" is the story of how isolating it can be to watch everyone around you easily achieve something that seemes perpetually out of reach. It's my story, but I know it's also the story of so many others.

I wrote this book to give families that experienced infertility an empowering way to share that history with their child. Let this book be one that you come back to time after time to remind you of how far you've come. And if you're still waiting for your turn, know that I am cheering you on from afar. 💜

It's imperative that the full range of healthcare options are available to those who are trying to build a family. That's why a portion of the proceeds from this book will go to RESOLVE's Fight for Families campaign, which is focused on protecting access to IVF and other family-building options.

My endless gratitude goes to Dr. Kaplan, the laboratory team and everyone at Fertility Centers of Illinois for all you do every day to make dreams come true.

-Erin Sarris, author
@erinsarriswrites
cupcakeseverywhere.com

A Note From An Infertility Specialist

A parent-child relationship is a unique bond, the consequences of which manifest at every level of one's life.

Having experienced, as a physician specializing in the IVF world, the evolution of this transformative technology over the past 30 years, I believe this book has been written at a critical juncture.

Millions of children globally have been conceived through IVF and its related technologies, and in many ways reflect our continuous progress in society.

Heterosexual couples with infertility, the LGBTQ+ community, utilization of donor eggs, donor sperm and gestational carriers, single parenting — they are all part of this superb mosaic.

This book is a wonderful contribution to our field, allowing young children to understand conception in its various forms, normalizing the technology and subsequently benefitting us all in society.

Thank you for your contribution to a world I feel privileged to have contributed.

-Dr. Brian Kaplan,
Reproductive Endocrinologist
at Fertility Centers of Illinois

About the Author

Erin Sarris is a writer who lives in Chicago with her family, which includes her husband and their twins conceived through many rounds of IVF — followed by a surprise singleton cupcake.

This is her first children's book.

About the Illustrator

Bessa (Barbora Dzadík Kmecová) is a female illustrator from Slovakia whose work explores the limits of vector graphics. She creates out-of-scale, dynamic and highly conceptual visuals with humor and light irony.

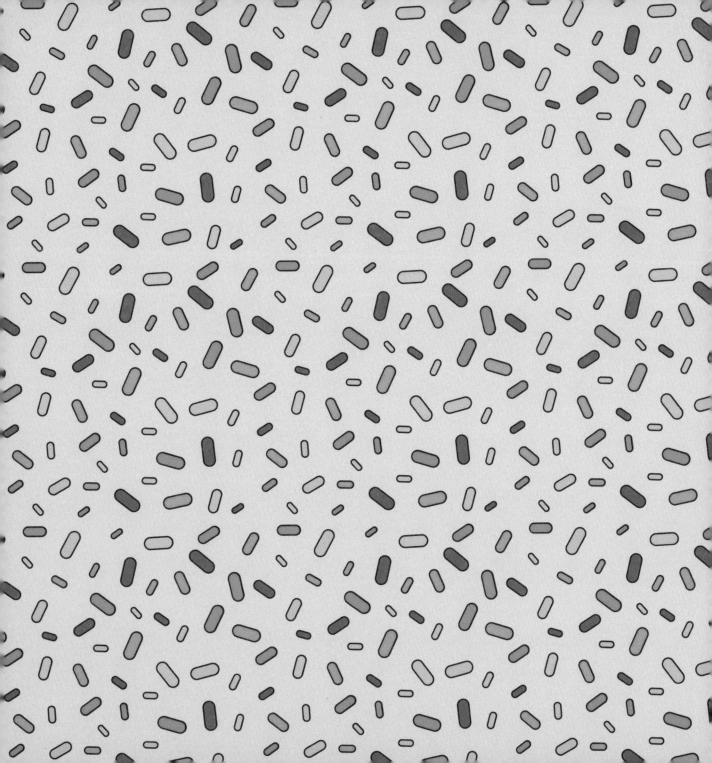